Orion Books Ltd

Orion House

5 Upper St Martin's Lane

London WC2H 9EA

First published by Orion 1998

Drawings by Michael Martin

Cover illustrations by Alex Graham

© Associated Newspapers plc 1998

ISBN 0 75281 738 8

Printed and bound in Great Britain
by The Guernsey Press Limited.

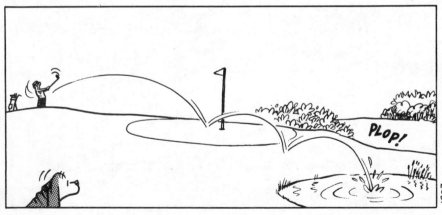

HEY, LUKE, IT'S THAT YELLA BELLY BASSET!

Uh-oh, the Tucker twins are at it again

WE'RE TAKIN' YA IN — PUT YER HANDS UP!

?

Will my paws do?